Monty was a monster, a big friendly monster.

His little friend, Titch, was a friendly monster too.

One day Monty and Titch went to the seaside.

They saw a boat on the sand.

Monty wanted to go in the boat.

'Can you help?' said Monty.

'Yes, I can help,' said Titch.

'I can see a fish,'
said Monty.

'Can you?' said Titch.

'I can see a big fish,'
said Monty.

'It is a shark!' said Titch.

'Help!' said Monty.